SJ

 # Welcome!

All of the ingredients in this book are safe to use,
but make sure you always follow these rules...

Before You Start

* Read the instructions before starting, and follow them carefully.

* Gather all the ingredients and equipment before you start.

* Don't use any ingredients not listed in the recipes and make sure an adult has checked them over before you start sliming.

* Any slime making should be done under adult supervision. We've highlighted times when a grown up should do something for you.

* No snacking around the slime-making area, and when we say slimes cannot be eaten – we mean it!

* Keep children under 3 years old and all animals away from your slime experiments.

* Wear eye protection and keep slimy hands away from your eyes.

* Only make and play with slime on hard surfaces – keep away from furniture, carpets, and other delicate items that are hard to clean.

* Always store your slime in an airtight container (see p64) and place in the fridge. Throw it away after a week. Some slimes will need to be thrown away straight after play - check the recipe instructions carefully.

* Watch out when using paint or food colouring – it can stain. Wear rubber gloves so you don't stain your hands.

* Always wash your hands before and after making and playing with slime.

* Clean up after yourself! Wash all equipment and surfaces (see p64).

* A lot of the slimes use eyewash solution. Make sure you use this and not lens cleaner or contact lens solution.

* Don't throw your slimes down the sink or toilet after you've finished with them - throw them in the bin.

SUPER SLIME

DK

Penguin
Random
House

Editor Sophie Parkes
Jacket designer Elle Ward
Pre-production producer
Dragana Puvacic
Senior producer Amy Knight
Managing art editor Gemma Glover
Creative director Helen Senior
Publisher Sarah Larter

Written, designed, edited, and
project-managed
for DK by Dynamo Ltd.

First published in Great Britain in 2019 by
Dorling Kindersley Limited
80 Strand, London, WC2R 0RL

A CIP catalogue record for this book
is available from the British Library.
ISBN: 978-0-2413-8742-9

Printed in Romania

A WORLD OF IDEAS:
SEE ALL THERE IS TO KNOW

www.dk.com

Acknowledgements:
The publisher would like to thank the following people for
their help in photographing, making, and handling slime:
Mia Pestridge, Leo Sandford, and Kate Ford.

All photography © Tim Pestridge/DK

Cover images: **Front:** Depositphotos Inc: Kamonrat;
Back: Depositphotos Inc: Kamonrat

Welcome!

Slime fun is waiting just over the page,
but remember:

* **None of the recipes in this book are edible –
DO NOT eat them.**
* **All recipes containing food must be thrown
away on the day you play with them. Take
extra care when handling raw egg.**
* **Always wash your hands thoroughly before
and after handling slime.**
* **All of our recipes use biodegradable glitter.**

Contents

Basic Slime Kit

Most of the recipes in this book need the following items...

bowls

measuring spoons

clear craft glue

PVA glue

mixing spoon or spatula

cornflour

eyewash

bicarbonate of soda

shaving foam

. . . .

Here are some of the extras you'll need. Check each recipe for specific ingredients.

buttons

plastic beads, gems and pompoms

washing up liquid

felt-tip pens

biodegradable glitter

shimmer dust

. . . .

Most ingredients in this book are easy to find, but if you can't get certain items, ask an adult to buy them or order them online.

Playdough Slime

If you're new to slime, this is a great recipe to get you started. With only a few ingredients, it's super easy and fun!

YOU WILL NEED

* 235 ml (8 fl oz) hair conditioner
* 5 drops of food colouring
* 470 g (16 oz) cornflour

1

Squeeze the hair conditioner into a mixing bowl and stir in the food colouring.

2

Mix in the cornflour. If the mixture is still wet, add in more cornflour gradually and keep mixing as you go!

3

Knead and squish the slime with your hands until it feels like dough.

TIME:
10 MINUTES

DIFFICULTY:
EASY

WARNING:
NON-EDIBLE

SCIENCE BIT!

Do you want to know why
we add cornflour? It helps to
bind and thicken mixtures.
As well as being used for slime,
cornflour can be used in custard,
gravy, and lots of other sauces.

⚠ MAY STAIN!

Butter Slime

This slime can be spread with a knife, just like butter! It's so good you'll want to share the recipe with all your friends.

YOU WILL NEED

* 240 ml (8 fl oz) PVA glue
* 1 tsp bicarbonate of soda
* 3 tbs water
* 2-3 drops food colouring
* 1 tsp baby oil
* 2 tbs baby lotion
* 1 tbs eyewash – it must contain boric acid and sodium borate
* 2-4 tbs cornflour

1

Pour the PVA glue into a bowl and mix in the bicarbonate of soda and water. Then stir in your food colouring.

TIME:
10 MINUTES

DIFFICULTY:
EASY

WARNING:
NON-EDIBLE

⚠ MAY STAIN!

2

Mix in the baby oil and baby lotion.
Next, beat in the eyewash.

The mixture will probably still be sticky, so add the cornflour
and stir until you can start to knead it with your hands.
The more you knead, the less sticky it will become!

3

Toothpaste Slime

Do you want a slime that smells minty fresh? This is the recipe for you!

YOU WILL NEED

* 4 tubes (about 500 ml total) of toothpaste
* baby lotion
* 250g (9 oz) cornflour
* baby oil

1

Squeeze the toothpaste into a microwave-safe bowl and heat for 16 minutes, getting an adult to stir it regularly. Be careful, as it gets very hot! Leave this to cool for two hours.

⚠️ MAY STAIN!

2

When cool, stir in the baby lotion a little at a time to make a smooth texture. Then, add the cornflour until the mixture becomes crumbly.

3

Gradually add the baby oil until the slime texture becomes smooth. Be careful not to make it too oily!

TIME:
2 HOURS, 10 MINS

DIFFICULTY:
INTERMEDIATE

WARNING:
NON-EDIBLE

TOP TIP!

Ask an adult to stir the toothpaste regularly while it is in the microwave. This stops it burning or sticking to the bowl.

Egg-cellent Slime

Are you ready for a cracking good slime?
Here's all you need to know.

YOU WILL NEED

* 2 egg whites
* 60 ml (2 fl oz) washing up liquid
* glitter

2

Mix in the washing up liquid really well, then pop your slime in the fridge overnight (for at least eight hours) to set. If it's still runny, leave it for a few more hours.

1

Ask an adult to help you separate the egg whites from the yolks into a mixing bowl.

TIME:
OVERNIGHT

DIFFICULTY:
EASY

WARNING:
NON-EDIBLE

3

Your slime should now feel squishy.
It's time to add some glitter and start
playing with your creation.

SAFETY FIRST

Always wash your hands well after
handling this slime as it contains
raw egg! Don't keep this slime
for more than 24 hours.

MAY STAIN!

Slime Stress Balls

Make some clear slime and squeeze it into a balloon to make your own stress balls to play with!

YOU WILL NEED

FOR THE CLEAR SLIME

* ½ tsp bicarbonate of soda
* 120 ml (4 fl oz) warm water
* 140 ml (5 fl oz) clear craft glue
* eyewash – it must contain boric acid and sodium borate

FOR THE STRESS BALL

* balloons
* fruit or vegetable net bag

TIME:
10 MINUTES

DIFFICULTY:
EASY

WARNING:
NON-EDIBLE

Put the bicarbonate of soda and water into a bowl and mix in the clear glue.

Beat in small amounts of eyewash until the mixture turns gloopy. Add more eyewash if it is too sticky!

3

Push your clear slime mix into a balloon and tie up the end.

4

Wrap the net bag around the balloon. Enjoy squishing and squeezing your stress ball.

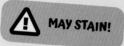 **MAY STAIN!**

TOP TIP!

Be careful not to overfill your balloon and make sure there are no big air bubbles inside before you tie it up.

Draw-on Slime

It's time to get arty! Make this stretchy white slime that you can doodle all over with your pens.

YOU WILL NEED

* 1 tsp bicarbonate of soda
* 240 ml (8 ½ fl oz) PVA glue
* 1 tbs eyewash – it must contain boric acid and sodium borate
* felt-tip pens

2

Next, stir in the eyewash. The slime should start to get stringy and come away from the edge of the bowl.

1

Pour the bicarbonate of soda and glue into a bowl and mix them together well.

3

Now it's time to start kneading and squishing the slime with your hands.

4

The slime should feel rubbery. Stretch your slime out and get drawing!

TIME:
10 MINUTES

DIFFICULTY:
EASY

WARNING:
NON-EDIBLE

Rhubarb and Custard

TIME:
10 MINUTES

DIFFICULTY:
EASY

WARNING:
NON-EDIBLE

This fab recipe shows you how to turn clear slime into rhubarb and custard-coloured swirls!

YOU WILL NEED

* clear slime ingredients (see pages 12-13)
* pink and yellow food colouring
* pink and yellow biodegradable glitter

1

Make your clear slime, and divide it into two bowls. Add pink food colour to one half, and yellow to the other.

⚠️ MAY STAIN!

TOP TIP!

You can try all kinds of colours to invent your own super slime. How about blue and green sea slime? Have fun experimenting!

2

Sprinkle lots of glitter onto each slime colour to make it shimmer. Use your hands to mix it together.

3

Lay your two slimes out into strips and mix the two colours together to make awesome swirls.

Avalanche Slime

Turn over your bowl of avalanche slime to watch it blend into magical colours!

YOU WILL NEED

* clear slime ingredients (see pages 12-13)
* stretchy slime ingredients (see pages 14-15)
* food colouring (try yellow and green)
* biodegradable glitter

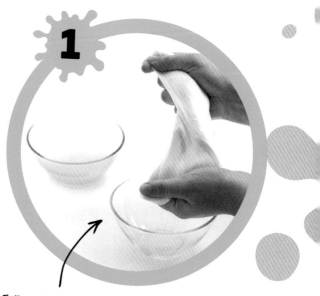

1

Follow the steps on pages 12-13 to make the clear slime, and pages 14-15 for the stretchy slime.

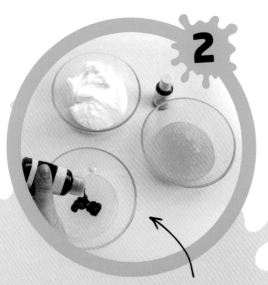

2

Split the clear slime in half and make each half a different colour using glitter and food colouring.

3

Put the two colours of slime into a bowl together and spread some stretchy slime on top.

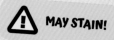
TIME:
40 MINUTES

DIFFICULTY:
EASY

WARNING:
NON-EDIBLE

Look at how
the white slime
blends with the
other colours!

4

Leave the slime
to settle for about
half an hour.

5

Now tip it out onto a plate
and watch the avalanche!

Galaxy Slime

This galaxy slime is out of this world!

YOU WILL NEED

* clear slime ingredients (see pages 12-13)
* pink, blue, black, and red food colouring
* glitter

1

Make clear slime using the recipe on pages 12-13. Now split your slime into four bowls and make each a different colour.

2

Add lots of glitter to each colour. It works best if you mix it in with your hands!

3

Lay out all the slimes and start twisting the colours together!

TIME:
10 MINUTES

DIFFICULTY:
EASY

WARNING:
NON-EDIBLE

TOP TIP!

Try adding star-shaped
sequins to your slime
for a cosmic effect!

Fish in a Bag

TIME:
10 MINUTES

DIFFICULTY:
EASY

WARNING:
NON-EDIBLE

With some toy fish and a freezer bag, you can transform blue slime into one of these incredible creations!

YOU WILL NEED

* **clear slime ingredients** (see pages 12-13)
* **blue finger paint**
* **ribbon**
* **freezer bag (with no holes!)**
* **plastic toy fish**

1

Make some clear slime using the recipe on pages 12-13, and mix in a blob of blue paint.

2

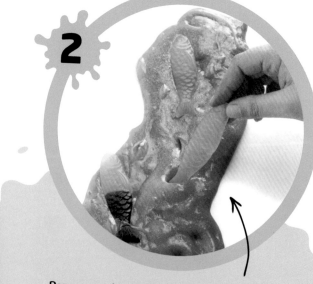

Pop some colourful toy fish into your slime.

3

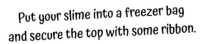

Put your slime into a freezer bag and secure the top with some ribbon.

This slime would make a fab gift for your friends.

TOP TIP!
. . . .
Try adding glitter or sequins to make shimmering water.

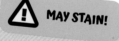

⚠ MAY STAIN!

Candy Cane

Want to know how to combine stretchy slime with clear slime? Here's a cool idea for how to do just that.

YOU WILL NEED

* clear slime (see pages 12-13)
* stretchy slime (see pages 14-15)
* red glitter
* red food colouring

1

Make a bowl of clear slime (see pages 12-13).

2

Mix up some stretchy slime (see pages 14-15).

TOP TIP!

You can make stripy colours with any combinations you fancy. How about mixing three colours?

Lay the two slimes out in strips and use your hands to twist them together in stripes.

4

3

Add red food colouring and glitter to the clear slime and mix it in.

TIME:
15 MINUTES

DIFFICULTY:
EASY

MAY STAIN!

WARNING:
NON-EDIBLE

25

Melted Snowman

This stretchy slime recipe is perfect for wintertime fun. Why stop at one snowman? You could make a whole family!

YOU WILL NEED

* 240 ml (8 fl oz) PVA glue
* 1 tsp bicarbonate of soda
* 1 tbs eyewash – it must contain boric acid and sodium borate
* buttons, pompoms, and a triangle of orange card to decorate

TIME:
10 MINUTES

DIFFICULTY:
EASY

WARNING:
NON-EDIBLE

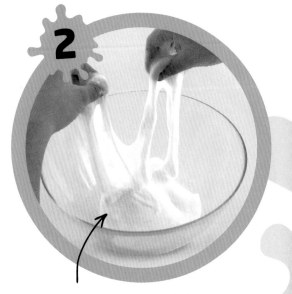

2

Beat in the eyewash until the slime starts to go stringy. Knead the mix with your hands. You should be able to pick it up without it sticking to you!

1

Pour the glue and bicarbonate of soda into your bowl and mix together well.

3

SCIENCE BIT!

SCIENCE BIT!

If you pull this slime slowly it stretches, but if you pull the slime quickly it can snap. It's all to do with the way the molecules in the eyewash and the glue stick together. Have a go for yourself!

Finally, stretch out your slime and put the button eyes, pompoms, and carrot nose in place. Your slime should look like a snowman that has melted across the table.

⚠ MAY STAIN!

Mash-up Slime

What happens when you bring together fluffy and clear slime? This mind-boggling mash-up, that's what!

YOU WILL NEED

FOR THE FLUFFY SLIME

* 480 ml (17 fl oz) shaving foam (not gel)
* food colouring of your choice
* 60 ml (2 fl oz) PVA glue
* ¼ tsp of bicarbonate of soda
* 1 tbs eyewash – it must contain boric acid and sodium borate
* small polystyrene balls

FOR THE CLEAR SLIME

* clear slime (see pages 12-13)
* glitter and sequins
* food colouring of your choice

1

Mix the shaving foam with a couple of drops of food colouring, then stir in the glue and bicarbonate of soda.

2

Next, whip in the eyewash until the mixture comes together and fold in some polystyrene balls.

TIME:
15 MINUTES

DIFFICULTY:
EASY

WARNING:
NON-EDIBLE

 **MAY STAIN!**

3

Make up some clear slime (page 12-13), and add food colouring, glitter and sequins.

4

Finally, mix the two slimes together and start playing!

TOP TIP!

This recipe works best if you make your fluffy slime a different colour to your clear slime. The two different textures are what makes this slime so fun to handle!

Festive Slime

TIME:
5 MINUTES

DIFFICULTY:
EASY

WARNING:
NON-EDIBLE

This recipe is great for when you're feeling festive. Have fun decorating your slime with heaps of colourful glitter and sequins!

YOU WILL NEED

* ½ tsp bicarbonate of soda
* 120 ml (4 fl oz) warm water
* 140 ml (5 fl oz) clear craft glue
* green food colouring
* eyewash – it must contain boric acid and sodium borate
* glitter, pompoms, and sequins

1

Mix the bicarbonate of soda and water together with the clear glue and green food colouring.

2

Stir in small amounts of eyewash until the slime starts to form. Then get your hands involved!

3

Lay out the slime and get crafty by sprinkling over glitter and sequins.

TOP TIP!
....

Go one step further and add a handful of pompoms to your festive slime. The more colours the better!

⚠ **MAY STAIN!**

Lucky Loom Slime

Up next is an awesome way to play with any extra loom bands you have hanging around!

YOU WILL NEED

* clear slime ingredients (see pages 12-13)
* loom bands
* glitter
* sequins

1

First, make some clear slime using the recipe and steps on pages 12-13.

2

Sprinkle in some glitter and sequins. Use your hands to mix them in well.

TIME:
10 MINUTES

DIFFICULTY:
EASY

WARNING:
NON-EDIBLE

⚠ **MAY STAIN!**

TOP TIP!
· · · · · · · · · · · · ·

Try adding food colouring, or putting different fun things in the slime – pom poms or super chunky glittter work really well.

3

Finally, add in a handful of colourful loom bands, mix, and your slime is ready!

Scented Slime

This slime smells so good you'll never want to put it down, but don't add too much peppermint or it might smell too strong!

YOU WILL NEED

* clear slime ingredients (see pages 12-13)
* red food colouring
* gold glitter
* 1 tsp peppermint essence

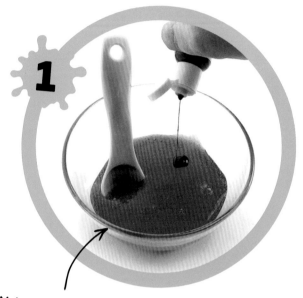

1

Make some clear slime using the recipe on pages 12-13 and stir in some food colouring.

⚠ MAY STAIN!

TIME:
5 MINUTES

DIFFICULTY:
EASY

WARNING:
NON-EDIBLE

Finally, add in a drop of peppermint essence and mix it in well.

3

Sprinkle in as much gold glitter as you like.

2

TOP TIP!

If you like adding a scent to your slime, you could try experimenting with different ones. How about vanilla extract? Although these slimes smell delicious, don't eat them!

Fake Vomit

TIME:
10 MINUTES

DIFFICULTY:
EASY

WARNING:
NON-EDIBLE

WARNING: Things are about to get totally gross! This fake vomit is sure to make your friends and family squirm. So, bring on the yuck!

YOU WILL NEED

* ½ tsp bicarbonate of soda
* 120 ml (4 fl oz) warm water
* 140 ml (5 fl oz) clear craft glue
* eyewash – it must contain boric acid and sodium borate
* lentils
* yellow and brown food colouring

1

Mix the bicarbonate of soda and water together in a bowl.

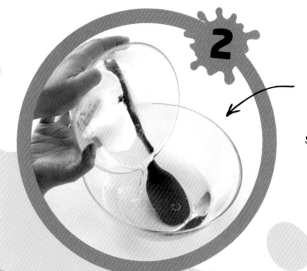

2

Add in the clear glue and stir in a little eyewash at a time until a gloopy slime starts to form.

3

Squirt in a few drops of food colouring, then use your hands to squish in some lentils.

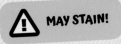

MAY STAIN!

SAFETY FIRST

This slime doesn't last for long. Play with it and then throw it away on the day you make it. Only make slime on a wipe down surface and never play with it near carpets as it can stain and damage furniture. Always ask a grown-up to help you.

Radioactive Slime

Grab some luminous green food colouring to bring this bubbling recipe to life.

YOU WILL NEED

* 120 ml (4 fl oz) warm water
* ½ tsp bicarbonate of soda
* 140 ml (5 fl oz) clear craft glue
* eyewash – it must contain boric acid and sodium borate
* lime green food colouring

1

Put your water and bicarbonate of soda into a bowl and mix in the clear glue.

2

Gradually drop in the eyewash and stir well until the mixture turns gloopy. Add a drop or two of food colouring until you get the radioactive look you want!

3

Beat the mixture with
a spoon or spatula until
your slime is thick enough
to be handled.

TIME:
5 MINUTES

DIFFICULTY:
EASY

WARNING:
NON-EDIBLE

Dish Soap Slime

This bubbly recipe proves that washing up liquid can be fun after all!

YOU WILL NEED

* 2 tbs washing up liquid
* 2 tbs clear glue
* ½ tsp eyewash – it must contain boric acid and sodium borate
* glitter

TIME:
5 MINUTES

DIFFICULTY:
EASY

WARNING:
NON-EDIBLE

⚠️ **MAY STAIN!**

Mix the washing up liquid and clear glue together.

3

Slowly drop in the eyewash and stir
it until the slime begins to form.

2

Finally, add in some glitter and
your slime is ready to play with!

Colour-changing Slime

Sunshine is all you need to turn this snazzy slime ALL the colours!

Add the glue, then stir in small amounts of eyewash until the slime begins to form a big clear ball with bubbles inside.

YOU WILL NEED

* ½ tsp bicarbonate of soda
* 120 ml (4 fl oz) warm water
* 140 ml (5 fl oz) clear craft glue
* eyewash – it must contain boric acid and sodium borate
* UV colour-changing beads

2

Mix together the bicarbonate of soda and water in your bowl.

1

⚠ MAY STAIN!

TIME:
10 MINUTES
. . . .
DIFFICULTY:
EASY
. . . .
WARNING:
NON-EDIBLE

TOP TIP!
. . . .

Put your UV colour-changing beads in the sunlight to charge them up first. This will help them to show up better when they're added to the slime.

When it's all mixed in, see how the beads change colour outside on a sunny day.

3

Next, pour in your UV colour-changing beads.

4

INSIDE!

OUTSIDE!

Marbled Silver Slime

Follow these simple steps to find out how to create a shimmery, shiny slime marbled with silver.

YOU WILL NEED

....

* clear slime ingredients
  (see pages 12-13)
* blue shimmer dust or food colouring
* silver glitter

Make clear slime using the recipe on pages 12-13, then split it into two. Make one blob a bit bigger than the other and add lots of silver glitter to the bigger bit!

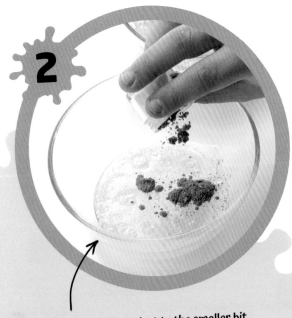

Add blue shimmer dust to the smaller bit.

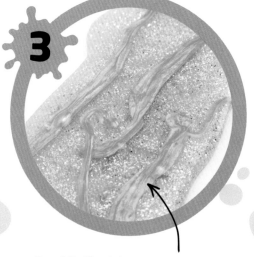

Carefully blend the two colours and use your hands to get stuck in.

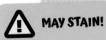

MAY STAIN!

TIME:
10 MINUTES

DIFFICULTY:
EASY

WARNING:
NON-EDIBLE

SCIENCE BIT!

All slime recipes need activating ingredients to make it work. These slime **activators** help turn glue into slime. Here the activator is eyewash, which chemically bonds with the glue when you mix it.

Halloween Slime

If you like everything spooky, you'll love this glow-in-the-dark slime!

YOU WILL NEED

* ½ tsp bicarbonate of soda
* 120 ml (4 fl oz) warm water
* 140 ml (5 fl oz) clear craft glue
* eyewash – it must contain boric acid and sodium borate
* glow-in-the-dark finger paint
* toy spiders

Beat the mixture until your slime stops sticking to the bowl.

Mix together the bicarbonate of soda, water, and glue. Add a dollop of glow-in-the-dark paint and stir in the eyewash a little at a time.

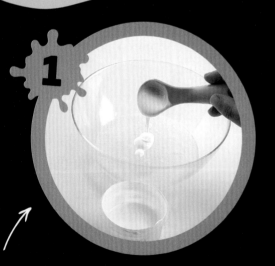

Add the toy spiders and switch off the lights to see the results! Don't forget to wash your hands when you've finished playing.

3

TIME:
10 MINUTES
. . . .
DIFFICULTY:
EASY
. . . .
WARNING:
NON-EDIBLE

TOP TIP!
. . . .
Charge up your slime under a lamp or in natural daylight, then it'll be ready to glow bright after dark!

Springtime Slime

Transform a bowl of clear slime into something sparkly and full of flowers. Just follow these simple instructions!

YOU WILL NEED

* ½ tsp bicarbonate of soda
* 120 ml (4 fl oz) warm water
* 140 ml (5 fl oz) clear craft glue
* eyewash – it must contain boric acid and sodium borate
* flower confetti or floral decorations
* glitter

1

Mix the bicarbonate of soda and water in your bowl.

TIME:
10 MINUTES

DIFFICULTY:
EASY

WARNING:
NON-EDIBLE

 **MAY STAIN!**

2

Stir in the clear glue and add small amounts of eyewash until the slime mixture gloops together. Mix in the glitter.

SCIENCE BIT!

Glue is made up of groups of atoms called polymers. When you mix it with eyewash the polymers stick together, turning the glue from a liquid into a solid.

3

Sprinkle lots of flower confetti or floral decorations to complete your springtime slime!

49

Fake Ice-cream Slime

Whip up this fake ice-cream slime in your fantasy ice-cream factory. Get creative adding sprinkles and toppings – but don't eat it!

YOU WILL NEED

* 2 tsp bicarbonate of soda
* 60 ml (2 fl oz) boiling water
* 240 ml (8 fl oz) clear glue
* 70 ml (2 ½ fl oz) cold water
* 1 tsp eyewash – it must contain boric acid and sodium borate
* 280 ml (10 fl oz) shaving foam
* plastic ice-cream cones
* sprinkles

1

Put the bicarbonate of soda into a jug, then carefully pour over the boiling water and mix it together. Leave this to cool.

2

In a separate bowl, mix the glue with the cold water and stir in the eyewash.

Then combine the two mixtures and leave to rest for half an hour.

TIME:
45 MINUTES

DIFFICULTY:
MODERATE

WARNING:
NON-EDIBLE

SAFETY FIRST!

Always ask a grown-up to help you with boiling water.

3

Next, start to fold in the shaving foam.

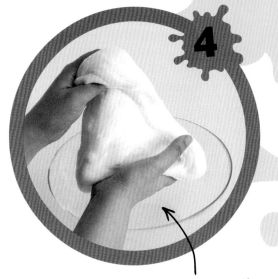

Top it off with colourful sprinkles!

4

Use your hands to knead the slime until it's fluffy.
Add a little more shaving foam if needed.

TOP TIP!
. . . .

Have a go at making
a different textured fake ice-cream
next! Check out this one we made using
the fluffy slime recipe on page 28.
What colours will you make?

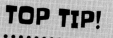

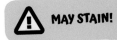 ⚠ **MAY STAIN!**

Mad Scientist Slime

Get ready to try out this bubbly slime step-by-step.
Once the foaming stops, you'll be left with a great slime!

YOU WILL NEED

* 60 ml (2 fl oz) distilled malt vinegar
* 1 tbs eyewash – it must contain boric acid and sodium borate
* a tray to put your foaming experiment on
* 140 ml (5 fl oz) PVA glue
* food colouring
* 1 tbs bicarbonate of soda

TIME:
15 MINUTES

DIFFICULTY:
INTERMEDIATE

WARNING:
NON-EDIBLE

⚠ **MAY STAIN!**

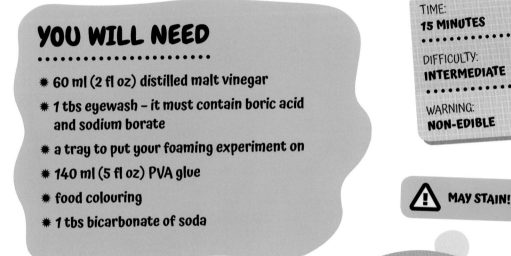

1

First, pour the vinegar into a bowl and stir in the eyewash. Leave this to stand.

2

Add the PVA glue to a separate jug, drop in the food colouring and give it a good mix. Put this onto a tray, then add the bicarbonate of soda.

Take the vinegar and eyewash mixture and pour this over the glue mixture. Quickly stir the mixture and watch as it starts to fizz up.

3

4

When the foaming stops you'll be left with slime to play with. Splash in a drop more eyewash if it's still too sticky to handle!

SCIENCE BIT!

When vinegar and bicarbonate of soda mix together, they react to form carbon dioxide bubbles. These bubbles increase the pressure inside the jug, and the bubbles start overflowing out of the top.

Banana Play Clay

Pick up that sad, forgotten banana from the fruit bowl and turn it into slime!

YOU WILL NEED

* 1 ripe banana
* cornflour
* 1 pinch of black fondant icing

SAFETY FIRST

This slime is NOT edible and it can only be played with on the day that you make it. Make sure you throw it away after play to avoid nasty smells.

1

Mash up your banana in a bowl with a fork.

TIME:
5 MINUTES

DIFFICULTY:
EASY

WARNING:
NON-EDIBLE

MAY STAIN!

Fold in some black
fondant icing to turn
the mixture grey.

Mix in cornflour a teaspoon at a time until you
can handle the slime without it falling apart.

Now it's time
to go bananas
with your play clay!

Ketchup Slime

Perfect on chips, perfect for slime. Who knew that ketchup was so multi-talented?

YOU WILL NEED

* about 2 tbs tomato ketchup
* 2 drops olive oil
* cornflour

SAFETY FIRST!

You must NOT eat ketchup slime. It's also important to know that this slime doesn't last long! Play with it on the day you make it, then throw it away to avoid any nasty smells.

2

Stir in a couple of drops of olive oil.

Simply squirt the tomato ketchup into a bowl.

1

3

Add the cornflour gradually until the mixture becomes less sticky. Then mix it with your hands!

TOP TIP!

This slime is all about experimenting and NOT for eating. It would taste horrid, so don't try it!

⚠ MAY STAIN!

TIME:
5 MINUTES

DIFFICULTY:
EASY

WARNING:
NON-EDIBLE

Glitter Masterclass

Here's a masterclass for perfecting your glitter technique! We'll show you how to layer up different types of glitter for the jazziest slime around.

YOU WILL NEED

* clear slime ingredients (see pages 12-13)
* lots and lots of glitter in different styles, shapes and sizes. Some finer shimmer dust and some chunkier versions work well together.

⚠ MAY STAIN!

1

Make clear slime using the steps on pages 12-13 and start mixing in fine green glitter.

TIME:
10 MINUTES

DIFFICULTY:
EASY

WARNING:
NON-EDIBLE

Look at these for colour and sparkle inspiration.

Next, sprinkle over different shades of green glitter into your slime and keep mixing it in. Don't be afraid to add a lot!

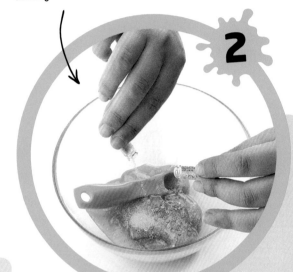

2

3

Next add chunkier glitter in similar colours. We've used blue and yellow star shapes!

TOP TIP!
....

You can add glitter to any slime recipe you like, but it works best of all in the clear slime. Have fun experimenting for yourself to see which you prefer.

60

Underwater Slime

Fill glistening blue slime with seashell confetti for this underwater slime.

YOU WILL NEED

* ½ tsp bicarbonate of soda
* 120 ml (4 fl oz) warm water
* 140 ml (5 fl oz) clear craft glue
* eyewash – it must contain boric acid and sodium borate
* seashell confetti
* sequins
* blue shimmer dust or food colouring

TIME:
10 MINUTES

DIFFICULTY:
EASY

WARNING:
NON-EDIBLE

⚠ MAY STAIN!

Mix the bicarbonate of soda with the glue and water. Then sprinkle in the shimmer dust.

Add small amounts of eyewash until the slime starts to gloop together.

3

Finally, add some sequins and colourful seashell confetti.

4

TOP TIP!

. . . .

If you don't have seashell confetti, you could add real shells or even little pebbles instead. Have a go for yourself!

Birthday Slime

This slime is ready to party. Pop it into party bags at your next birthday bash!

YOU WILL NEED

* clear slime ingredients (see pages 12-13)
* glitter
* balloon confetti

1

Make up a bowl of clear slime using the recipe on pages 12-13.

TIME:
10 MINUTES

DIFFICULTY:
EASY

WARNING:
NON-EDIBLE

3

⚠ MAY STAIN!

We mixed
purple with
pink glitter.

2

Pour in heaps of
your favourite
glitter colours!

4

Then add in
your balloon
confetti.

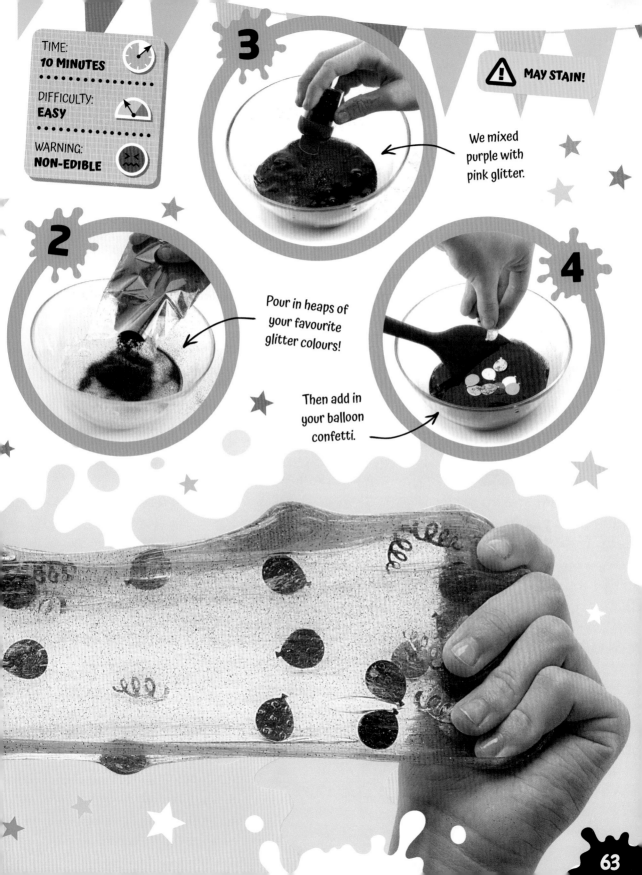

Slime Storage

Look after your slime carefully to stop it drying out. Make sure you store your slime in an airtight container in the fridge after play to keep it clean and slime-y. The slime may turn your container a different shade, so only use a tub that you're allowed to! Most slimes will last for up to a week, but some need to be thrown away straight after play, so check the information in the recipes carefully.

A plastic box with a lid is perfect.

Cleaning Up

You won't be popular if you make a mess, so follow these rules for a happy slime-filled home:

* Always make slime on a wipe-clean surface.
* There's always a risk of staining with paint or food colouring, so it's best to lay down some newspaper first.
* Mop up any spillages as soon as you can.
* Wash up all bowls and spoons as soon as you've finished.
* Wipe down all surfaces and put your slime kit and ingredients away.
* NEVER pour slime failures down the sink or toilet – you'll block the drains! Put them in the bin.
* Always ask an adult before using cleaning products or washing up liquid.

Hints and Tips

The recipes in this book should be easy to make, but slightly different ingredients may change the texture of the slime. With a bit of trial and error you should be able to get the results you want. Here are a few pointers:

 MY SLIME IS GOING HARD!
Slime doesn't last forever. Perhaps it's time to make your next batch? What will you make this time?

 MY SLIME BREAKS WHEN I STRETCH IT!
Sounds like you've added too much eyewash. Try squirting a small amount of the glue you've used onto your slime and carefully fold it in.

 MY SLIME ISN'T GLITTERY ENOUGH!
If you're using PVA glue, make sure you've got a chunky glitter rather than a fine one otherwise it will get lost. And remember, the key rule when making a glittery slime – add some glitter, then add some more!

 MY GLUE-BASED SLIME IS TOO STICKY!
Add a few drops of eyewash and mix well.